This is for Mum and Dad, with love.

With thanks to Joel Stewart, Emma Bonsall,
Portia Rosenberg, Woodrow Phoenix and Pam Smy.

Enormous extra special thanks to Faz and
to Lovely Ben Sharpe.

More brilliant books from the DFC Library:

THE SPIDER MOON
by Kate Brown

MEZOLITH
by Ben Haggarty & Adam Brockbank

GOOD DOG, BAD DOG
A DAVID FICKLING BOOK 978 1 849 92170 1

First published thanks to the amazing DFC weekly comic,
May 2008 – March 2009

Published in Great Britain in 2010 by David Fickling Books,
a division of Random House Children's Publishers UK
A Random House Group Company
This edition published 2013

1 3 5 7 9 10 8 6 4 2

Copyright © Dave Shelton, 2010

DAVID FICKLING BOOKS 31 Beaumont Street, Oxford, OX1 2NP

www.randomhousechildrens.co.uk
www.randomhouse.co.uk

Addresses for companies within The Random House Group Limited can be found at:
www.randomhouse.co.uk/offices.htm

THE RANDOM HOUSE GROUP Limited Reg. No. 954009

A CIP catalogue record for this book is available from the British Library.

Printed in China

The Random House Group Limited supports the Forest Stewardship Council® (FSC®), the leading international
forest-certification organisation. Our books carrying the FSC label are printed on FSC®-certified paper. FSC is the
only forest certification scheme supported by the leading environmental organisations, including Greenpeace.
Our paper procurement policy can be found at www.randomhouse.co.uk/environment

GOOD DOG, BAD DOG

Written & drawn by Dave Shelton

Golden Bone coloured by Faz Choudhury

David Fickling Books
OXFORD · NEW YORK

DOG MEETS DOG

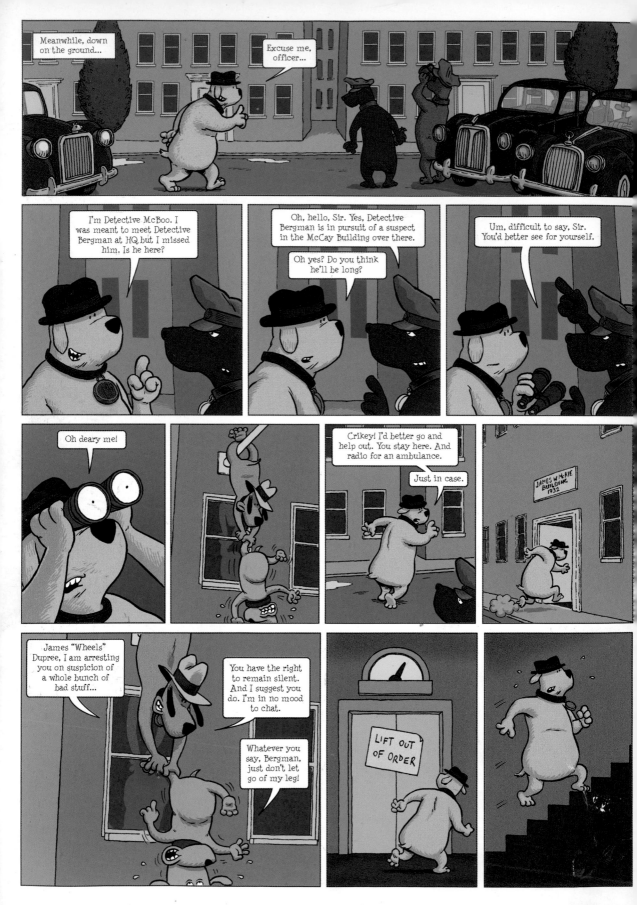

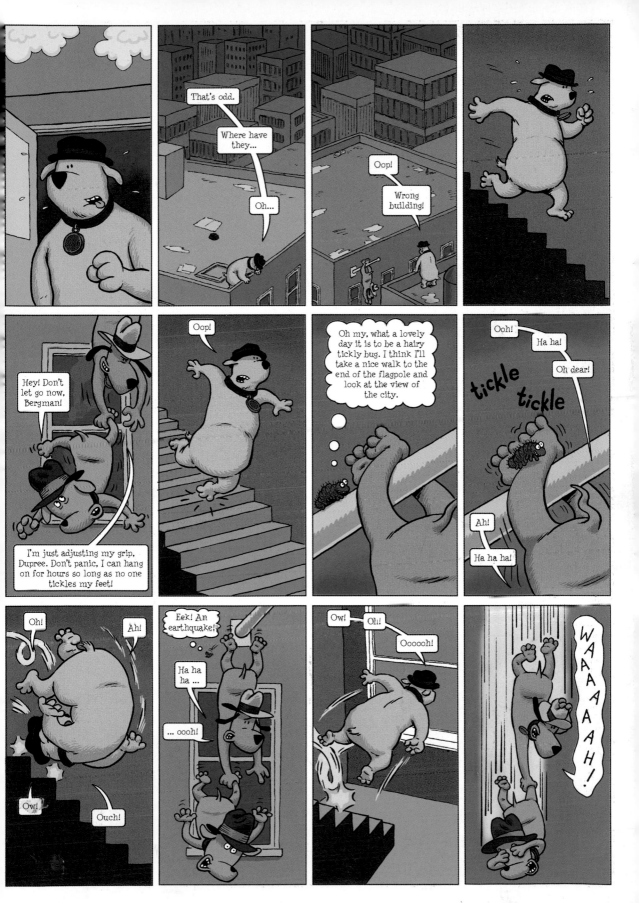

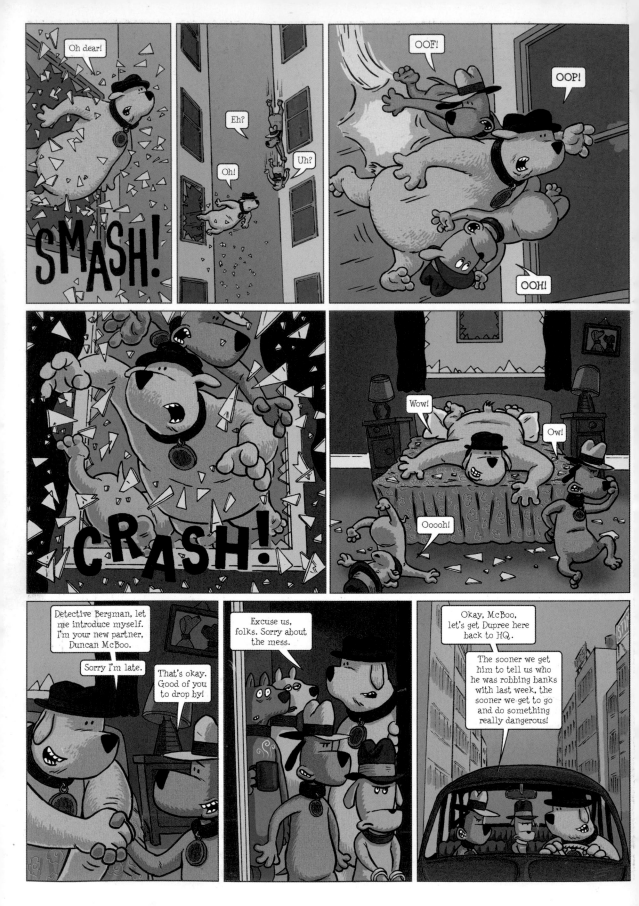

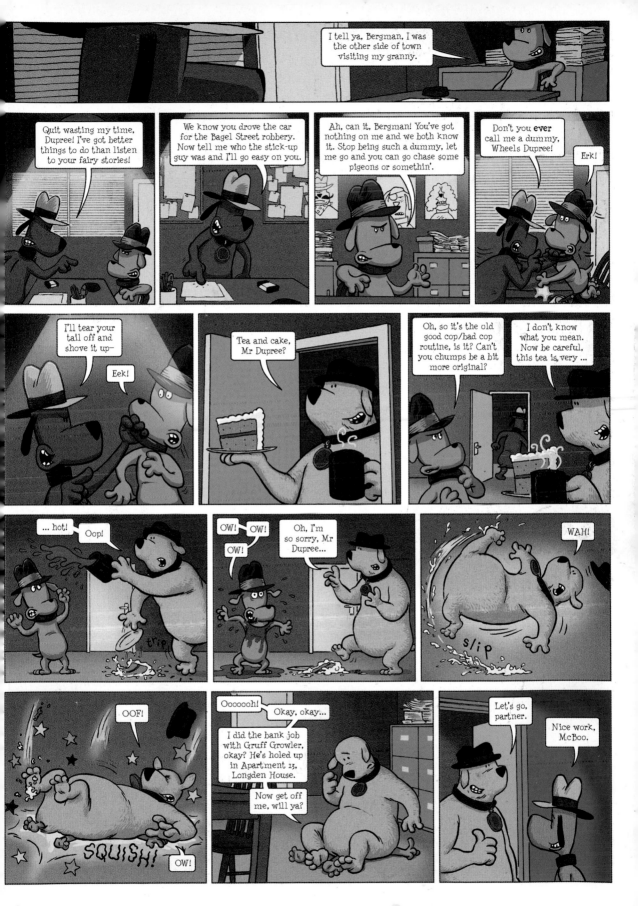

Longden House

BARKING
& WOOF

94,000, 95,000, 96,000... Ho boy!

Who's that?

KNOCK KNOCK

POLICE!

Open up, Growler!

Erk!

Luckily, I can make a quick exit down the old fire escape.

EEK!

Hello, Mr Growler, lovely day. Off out for a stroll?

Now, I'm afraid I am going to have to arrest you. I do hope that's okay?

Uh, yeah, sure thing, copper.

Oh good. I do so hate any ...

... unpleasantness.

Oh dear.

Stick 'em up, copper!

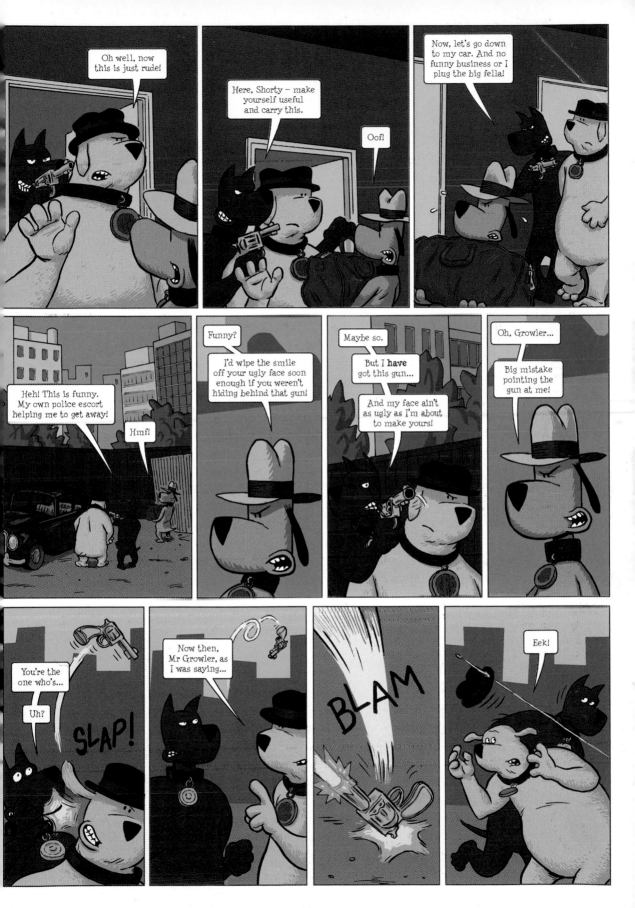

11

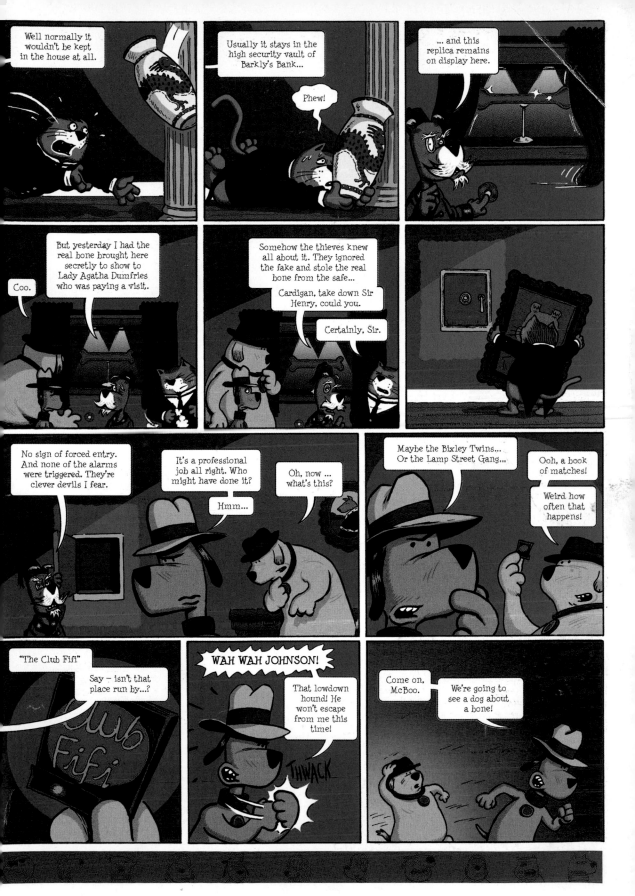

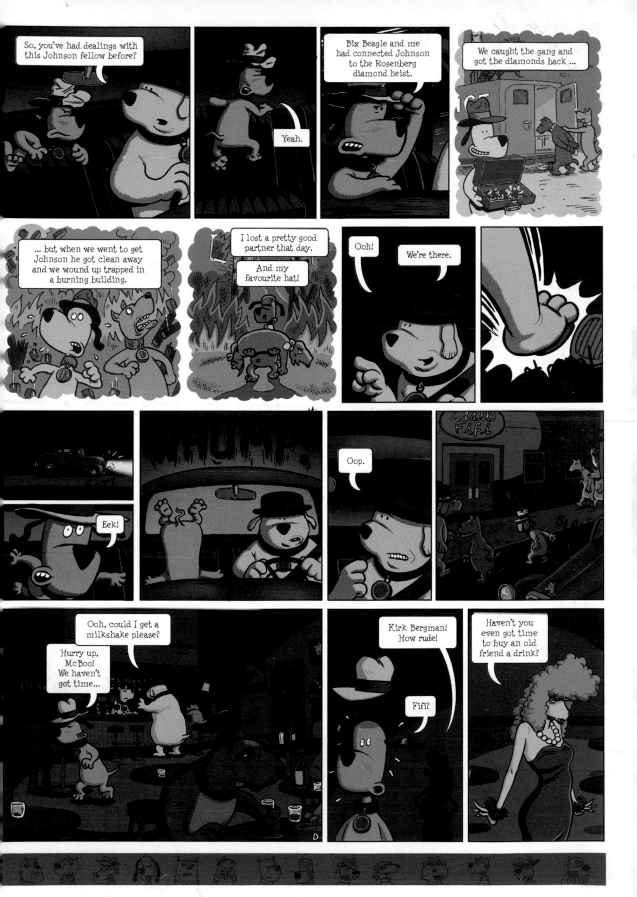

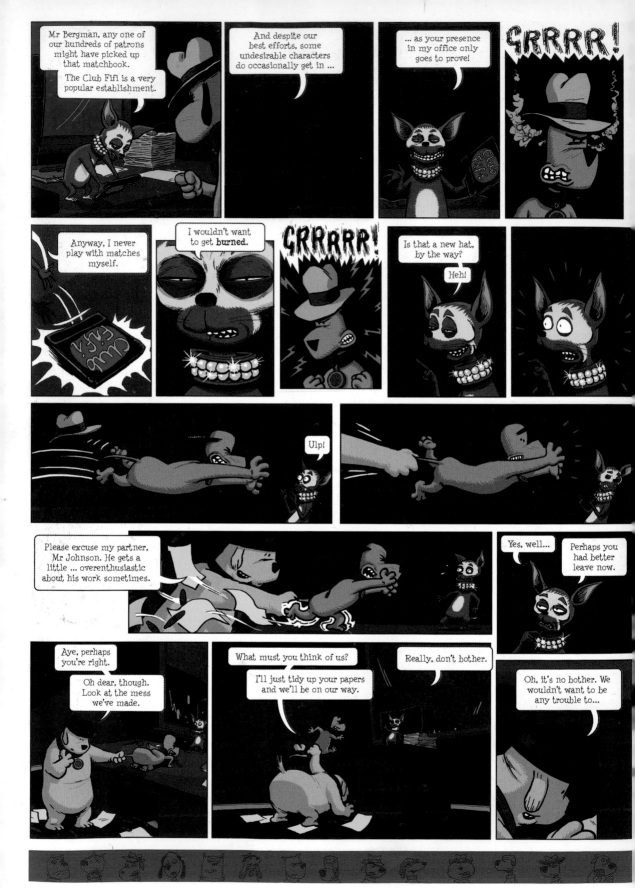

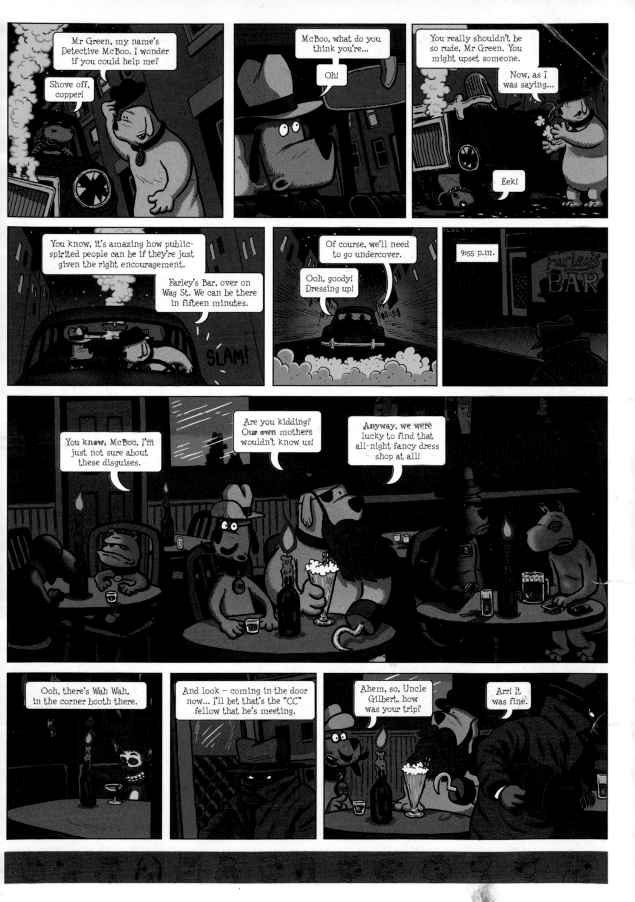

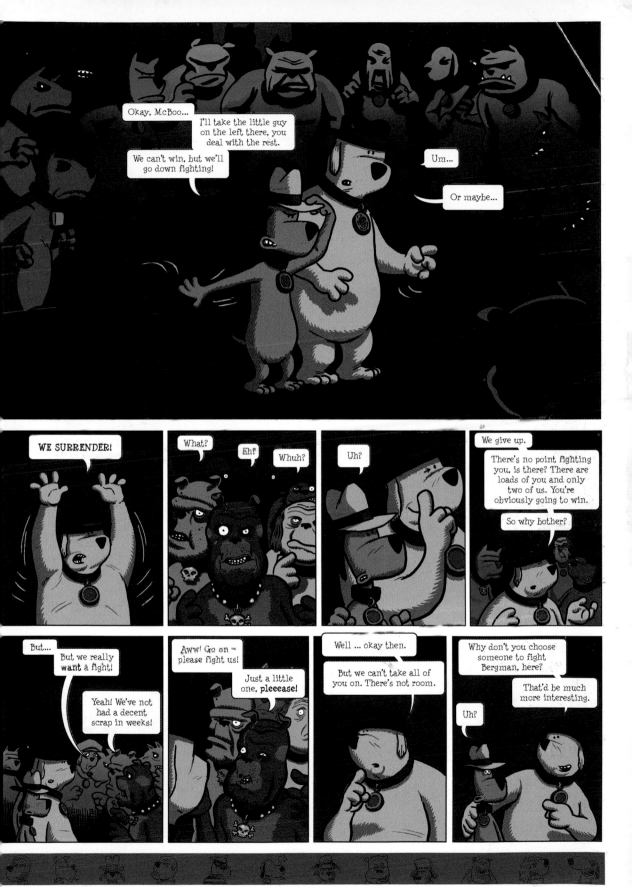

sproing

SPLASH!

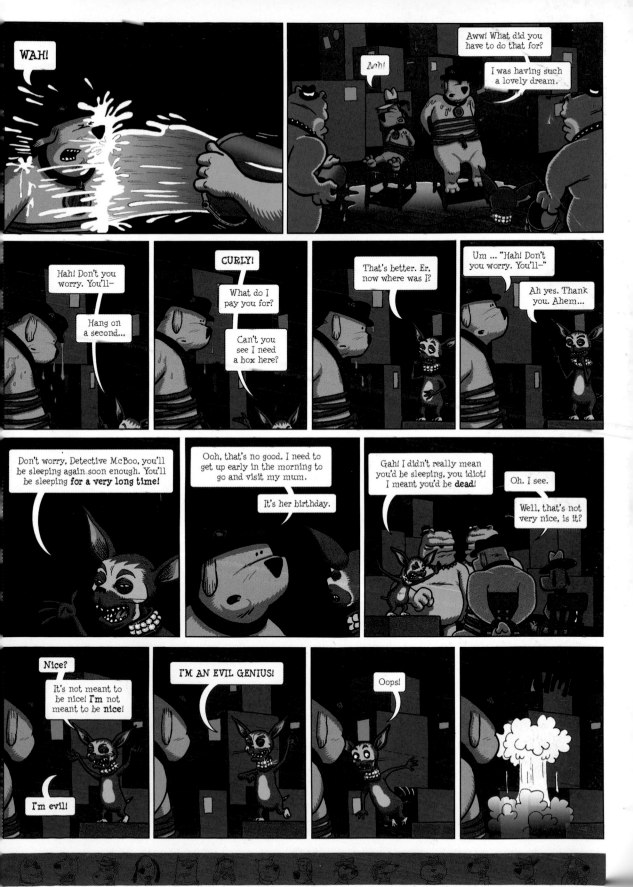

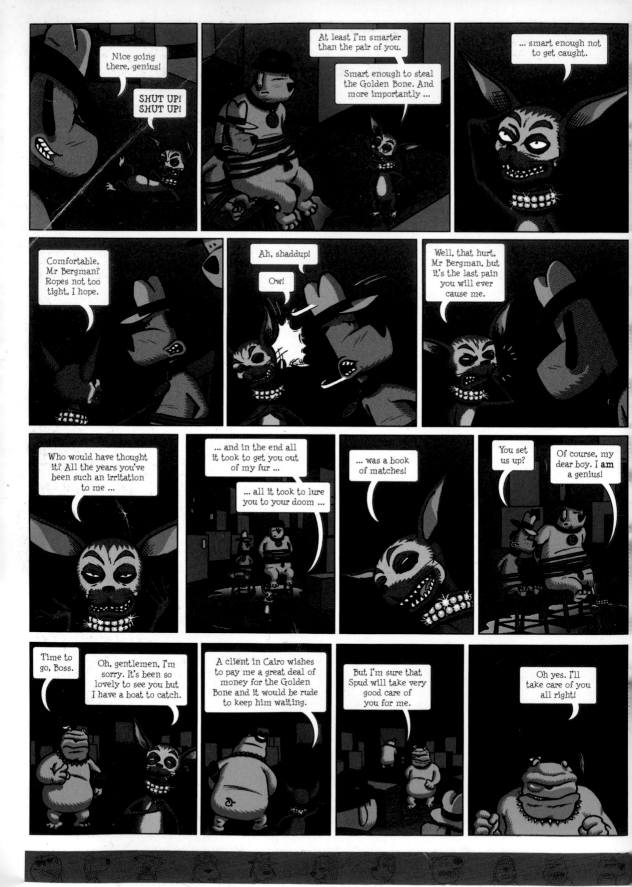

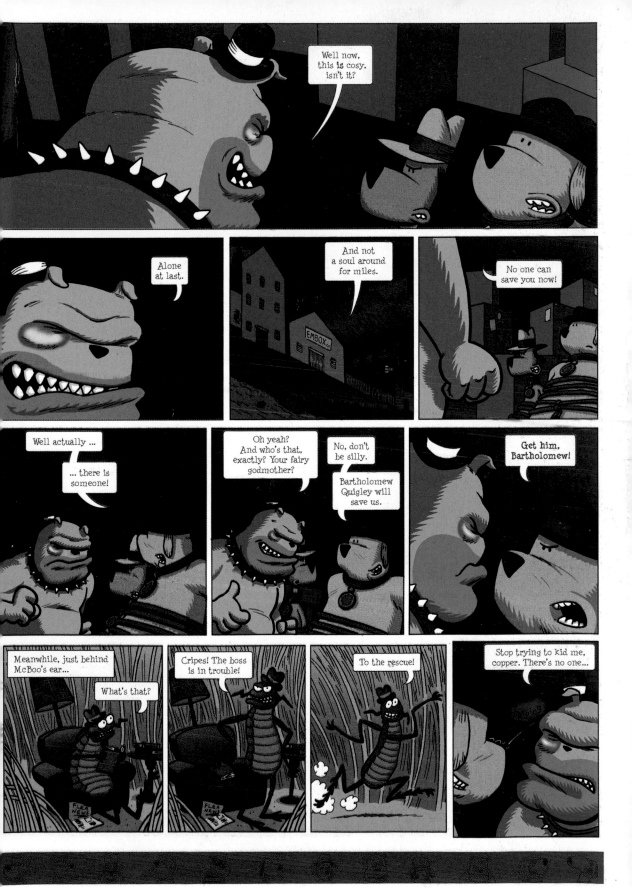

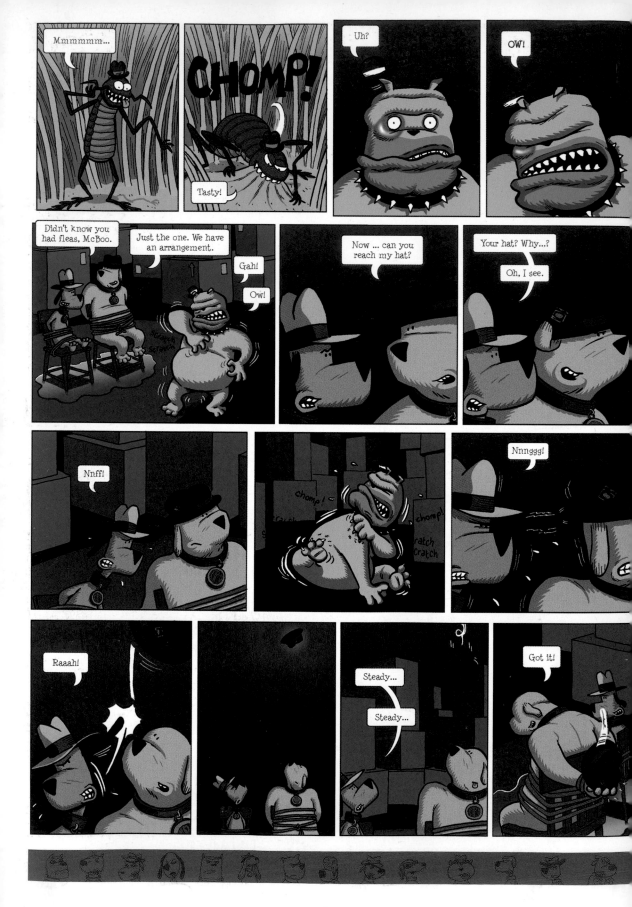

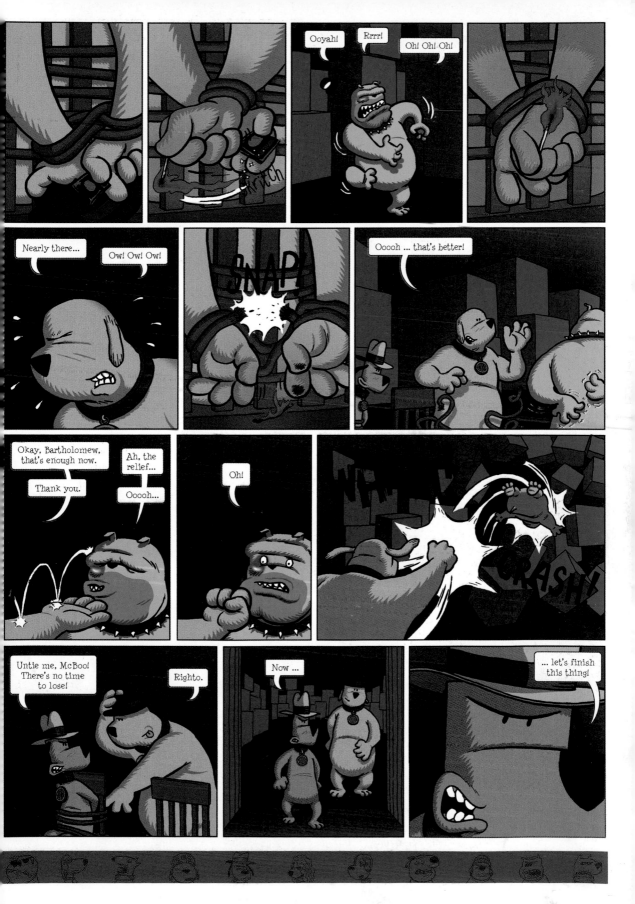

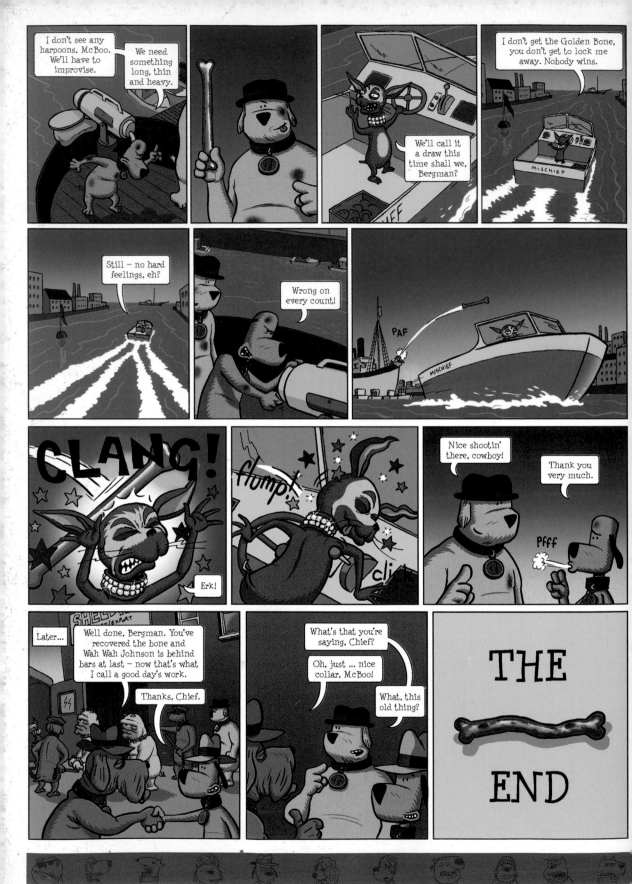

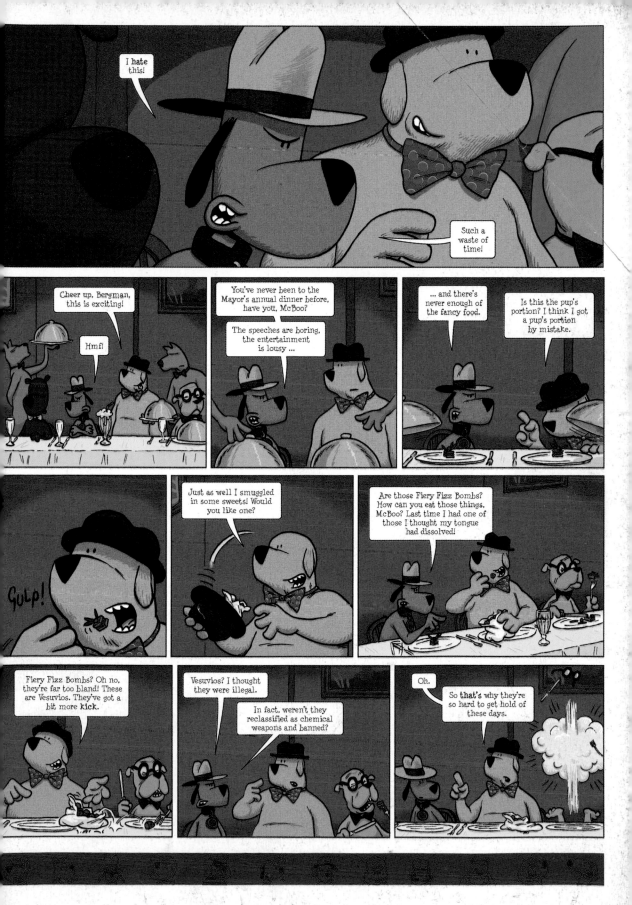

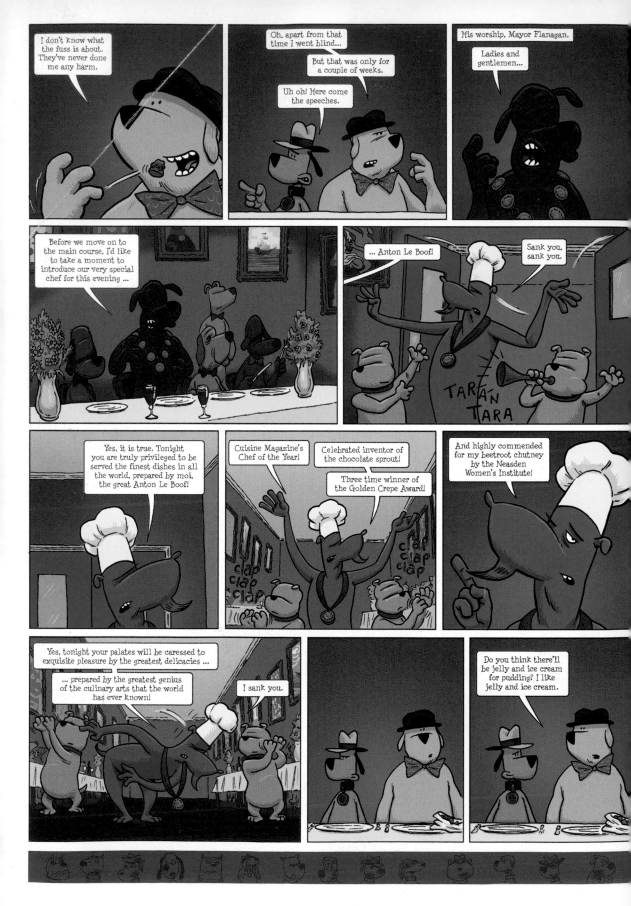

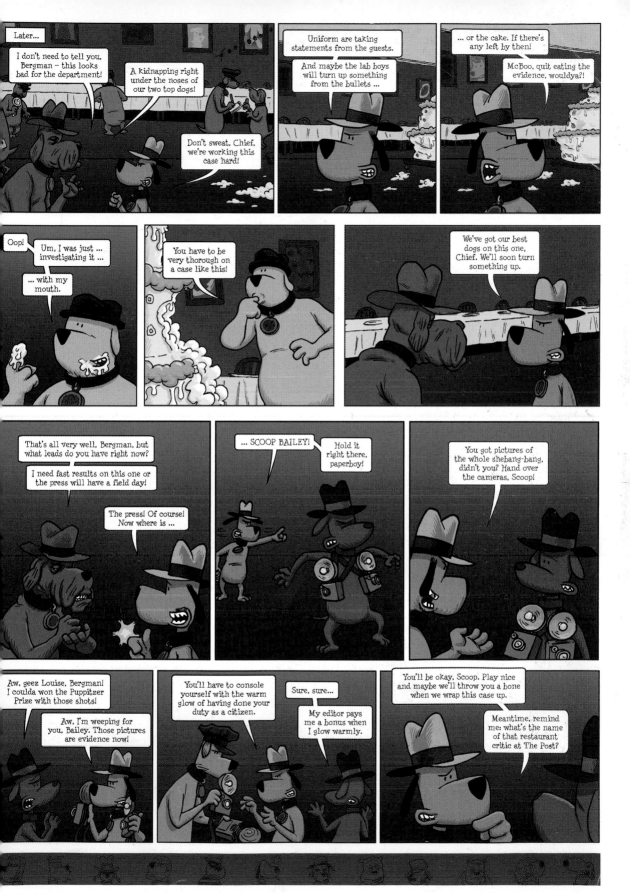

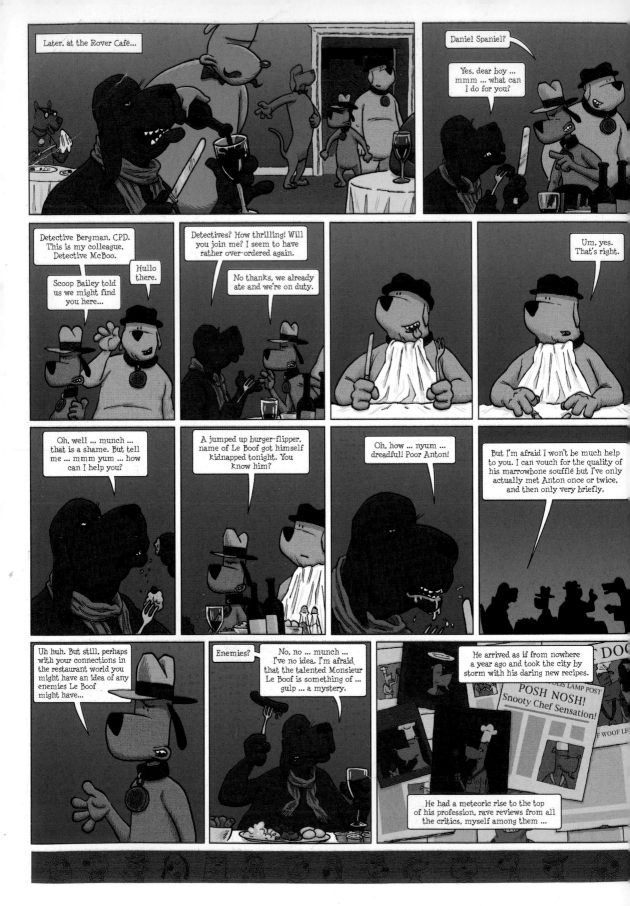

... but no scandal, no gossip, no enemies. Perhaps someone from his past but, as I say, his past is a mystery!

I see.

So sorry I can't be more help.

Detective Bergman, sir!

The lab sent me over with these for you. Said you wanted to see them as soon as possible.

Aha! Scoops's photos. Thanks, Officer Dooley.

No need to worry yourself, Spaniel. As you can see, we have other leads to work on.

Come on, McBoo.

Oh, righto. Bye bye, Mr Spaniel. Lovely to meet you.

A pleasure, dear boy.

CRASH!

ERK!

A SMASH!

Oop!

Sorry about that.

Come on, McBoo!

I shall have someone attend to the mess at once, Monsieur Spaniel.

Thank you, Marcel.

And could I have another bottle of the St Radegund '24, please.

And the telephone. There's a rather important call I need to make.

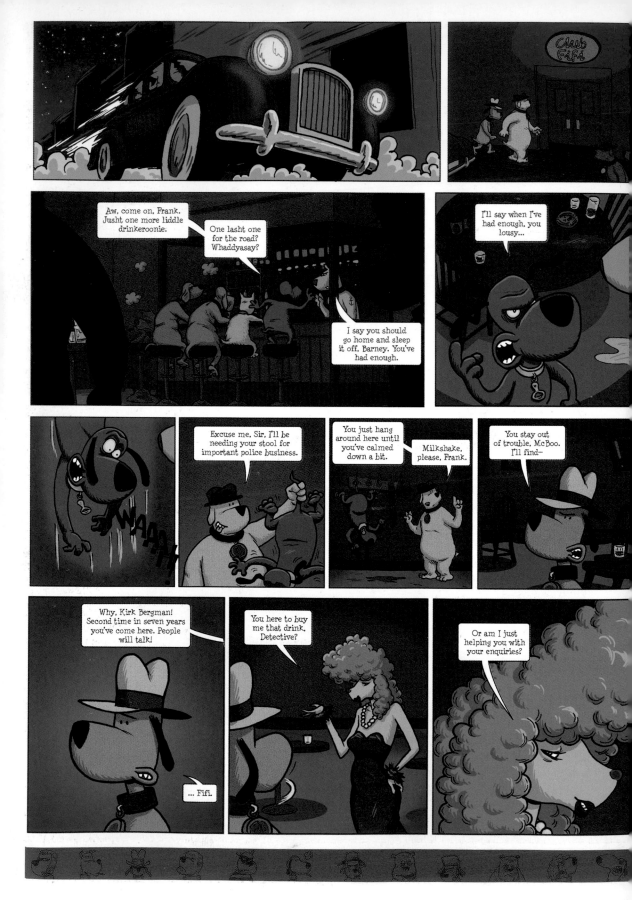

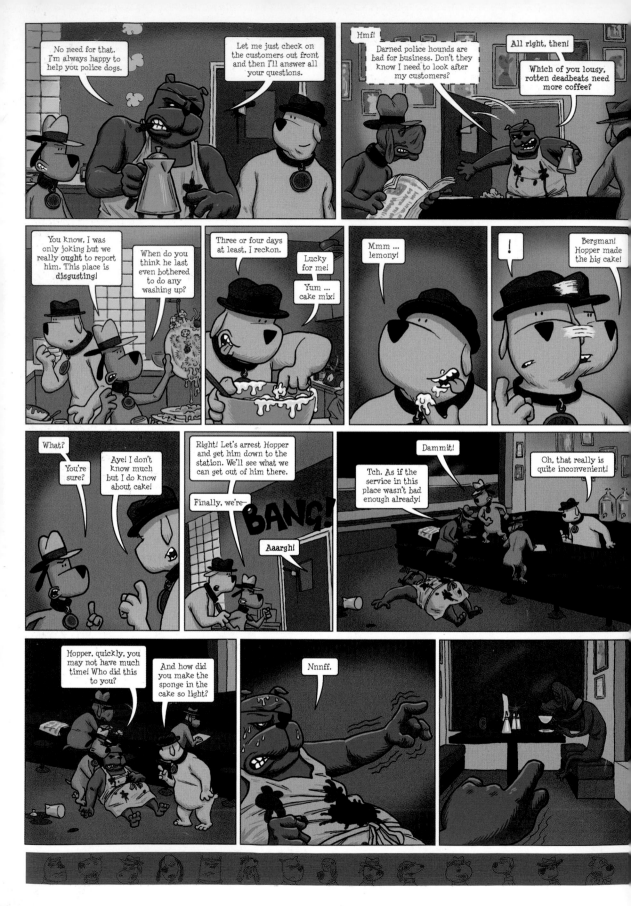

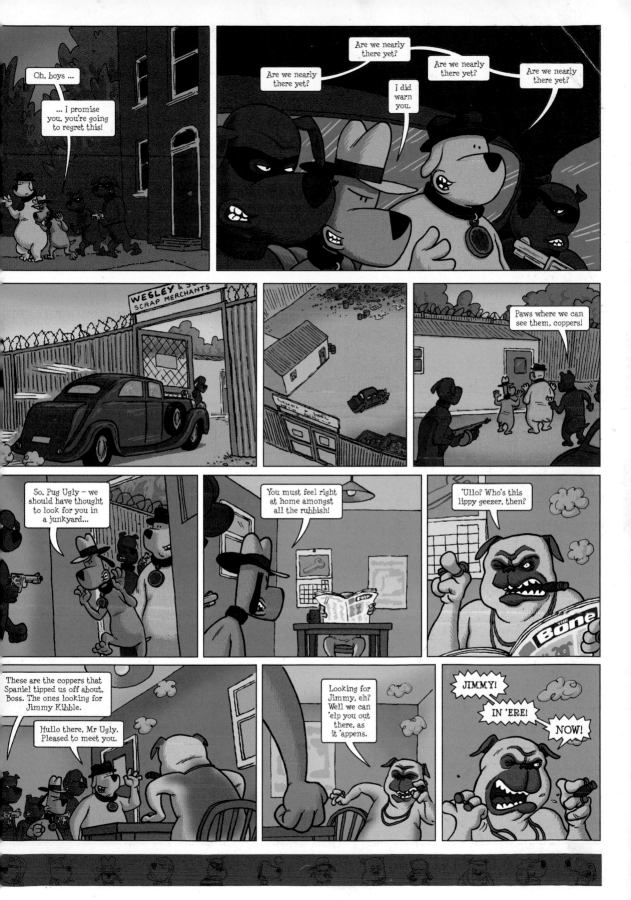

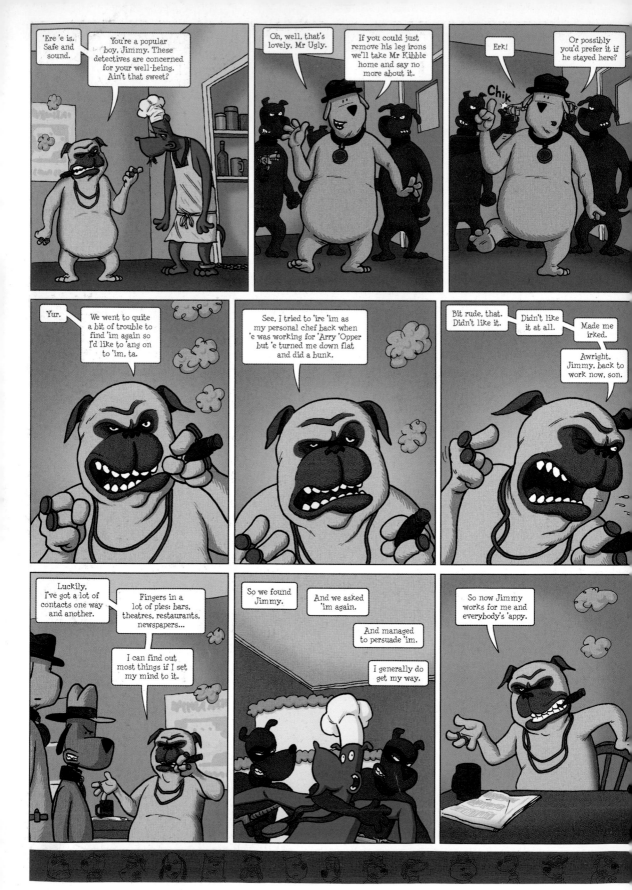

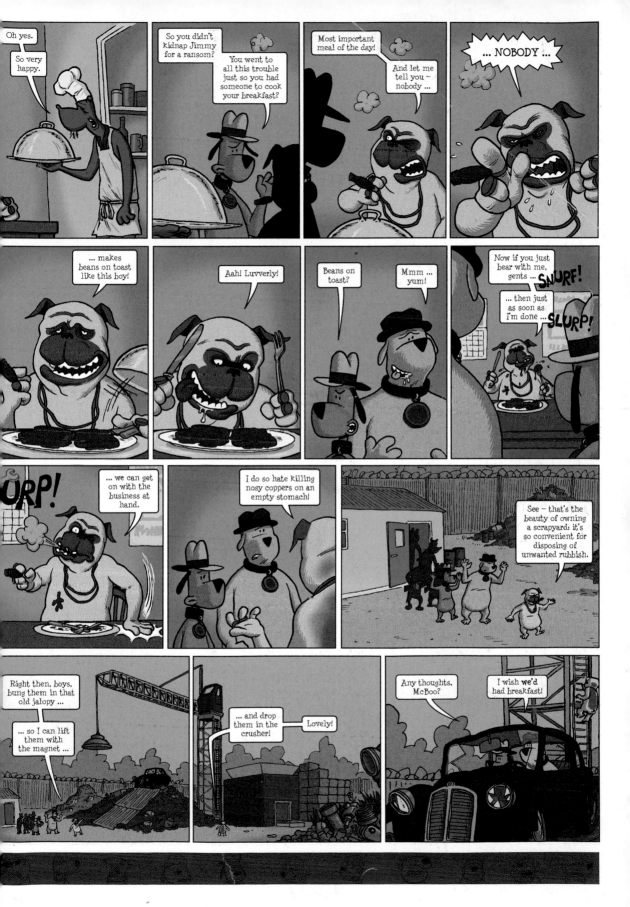

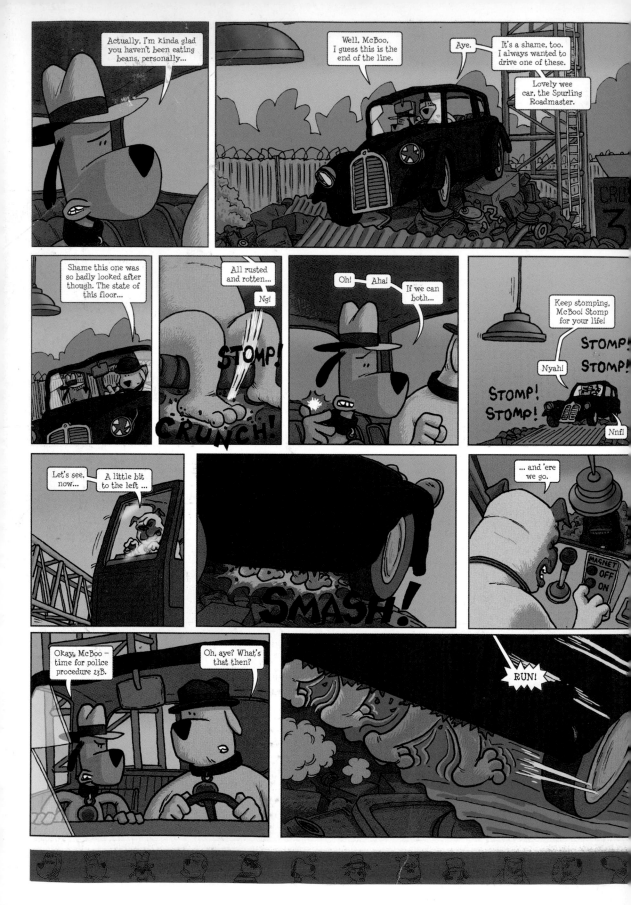